101
PANCHATANTRA
STORIES

Reprinted in 2016

An imprint of Om Books International

Corporate & Editorial Office
A-12, Sector 64, Noida - 201 301
Uttar Pradesh, India
Phone: +91-120-477 4100
Email: editorial@ombooks.com
Website: www.ombooksinternational.com

Sales Office
107, Ansari Road, Darya Ganj, New Delhi - 110 002, India
Phone: +91-11-4000 9000
Fax: +91-11-2327 8091
Email: sales@ombooks.com
Website: www.ombooks.com

ISBN 978-93-80070-77-3

Printed in India

10 9 8 7 6 5 4

101
PANCHATANTRA STORIES

Om
KIDZ

An imprint of Om Books International

Contents

1 The Swans and the Foolish Turtle

Once upon a time, a turtle and two swans were good friends. One year, there were no rains at all and the pond dried up. The turtle made a plan and told the swans, "Please look for a stick. I will hang on to the centre with my teeth as both of you hold the two sides of the stick and ferry me to another pond."

The swans said, "You have to keep your mouth shut all the time. Otherwise, you will crash to the ground."

When everything was ready, the swans flew off with the turtle. People who saw this sight exclaimed, "Look, how clever the swans are. They are carrying a turtle."

In trying to respond that it had been his idea, the turtle opened his mouth and fell to the ground and died.

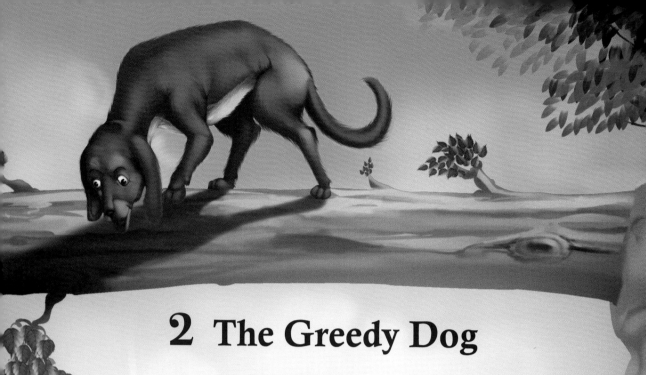

2 The Greedy Dog

While roaming around one day, a dog found a bone lying on the ground. He picked it up and quickly looked around him. Finding no one there to claim the bone, he ran away with it.

He then looked for a calm and quiet place to enjoy the bone. He reached a river and began crossing it by walking over a wooden bridge.

As he was crossing the bridge, he happened to look into the river and saw his own reflection in the water. He mistook the reflection to be another dog's.

He became greedy and wanted to snatch the other dog's bone as well.

In order to challenge the other dog, he barked at the reflection. In the process, as soon as he opened his mouth to bark, the bone in his mouth fell into the river. He tried to retrieve it but it was swept away by the current.

Thus, he lost even his own bone due to his greed of wanting more.

3 The Viper and the File

A viper went into a smith's shop in search of food. He peeped into every nook and corner but could not find anything edible. At last, he found a file. He started nibbling it. The file warned him to stop and go away.

The viper could not understand its meaning at first, but then the file turned to him and spoke out loudly to give him a warning again. "You're unlikely to get much from me," he said, "especially since it's my business to bite others. So stop nibbling me."

4 The Scholars and the Lion

In a small town, there once lived four brahmin scholars who were also great friends. Three of the scholars were very well-read. But the fourth one, while lacking in knowledge, was rich in common sense.

One of the scholars remarked to the others, "If we go to faraway courts of great kings, our wisdom will earn us fame and fortune."

The others immediately agreed. They all set out on a journey. On the way, they came across the skin and bones of a dead lion.

The first scholar said excitedly, "Let's test the power of our knowledge. Let's try and bring this dead lion back to life! I can put together its skeleton perfectly."

"I can fill the skeleton with flesh and blood," boasted the second scholar.

"I can bring his body to life so that it becomes a living creature," said the third scholar.

The fourth scholar said nothing about what he could do.

He resigned, shook his head and said, "Very well, you can please yourselves and do as you wish, but please wait till I climb up a tree. All of you are great scholars. I trust your wisdom and knowledge. You have the power to bring a dead beast to life and soon this lion will roar and be alive. However, I am not sure, if you have the power to change the nature of a beast. A lion never eats grass, as a lamb will never eat flesh."

His scholar friends laughed at him. "You seem to be scared for your life. Shame on you! You trust our knowledge, as you admit, but you have no idea, we enjoy complete control and command over the

creatures we create. Why
should the beast threaten us
when we are the ones to bring it to life?
Anyway, you are free to hide anywhere you like to
and watch us do our magic!"

The fourth friend quickly ran towards a tree and climbed
up on it as his friends still laughed at him.

When the third brahmin scholar breathed life into the lion,
the great beast stirred and awoke. Then, with a mighty roar, it
leapt upon the three scholars and ate them up in minutes. The
brahmin on the tree thanked God for giving him the common
sense not to mess with God and
his creations.

5 The Vain Stag

Once, there was a vain stag. He would often go to a pond to see his reflection and say, "What handsome antlers I have. But I wish I had beautiful legs too."

One day, a lion advanced towards him. He ran into the thick forest and his antlers got caught among the low branches of the trees. He realised that his end was now near, and cursed his antlers for that.

Finally, with the help of his strong legs, he was able to free himself from the branches. Thus, the stag managed to escape from the lion by running fast.

The stag realised that his ugly legs saved his life while his antlers could have been the cause of his death. Never again did he think that his legs were ugly.

6 The Crow and the Oyster

One day a hungry crow found an oyster on the beach. In order to eat the tasty meat inside, he tried to break open the oyster. He tried to use his beak to take out the meat, but failed to open the shell. Then he hit the oyster with a stone, but it remained tightly shut.

Meanwhile, another cunning crow came by and said, "My friend, the oyster will not open the way you are trying. I advise that you take the oyster in your beak and fly high into the air, then drop it onto the rocks below. Only then it will break open."

The hungry crow liked the idea and did the same.

As soon as the oyster shell broke open, the other crow picked it up and ate the meat inside.

By the time the first crow reached there, the meat was all over.

7 The Crane and the Crab

A big banyan tree was home to a number of cranes in a forest. In the hollow of that tree lived a cobra that used to feed on the young cranes. The mother crane used to cry for her offspring. Once a crab asked her, "What makes you cry?"

The crane told him everything and asked for some resolution. The crab thought to himself, 'These cranes are our born enemies. I shall give her advice that is misleading.'

So, the crab told the crane, "Strew pieces of meat from the mongoose's burrow till the hollow of the cobra. The mongoose will follow the trail of meat to the cobra and will kill it."

The crane did the same. The mongoose came and killed the cobra. But he also killed all the cranes on the tree.

8 The Dog in a Manger

There was a dog that lived in a barn. He would always sleep on the soft hay lying in the manger from which the horses ate their hay.

The dog's food used to be kept in the farmyard, outside the barn. Even then, the selfish dog would stay right there in the manger. Whenever the horses came in to eat their hay, the dog would start barking at them.

The poor horses could not eat their food. They asked the dog several times to leave the manger, but he always refused.

They told him that the farmer had left bones for him in the farmyard, but still he refused to move out of the manger.

"What a selfish dog!" the horses said. "He knows that he cannot eat hay but he will not let us eat our food too. He wants us to starve."

9 The Wolf as a Friend

Once, a wolf was following a flock of sheep. He noticed that the herdsman was guarding the flock closely, and decided it was best not to attack. Instead, the wolf decided to introduce himself. Initially, the herdsman was suspicious, but the wolf won him over with his amiable behaviour and soon became a part of the family.

One day the shepherd had to go to the town. He entrusted the wolf with the responsibility of guarding the flock. Once the shepherd left his place, the wolf pounced on the sheep and devoured them one by one. On returning, the shepherd understood what a fool he had been. He regretted his decision of trusting a wolf. A friend like a wolf is worse than an enemy.

10 Familiarity Breeds Contempt

One day, a fox saw a lion for the first time in his life. His long mane, formidable looks, scary roars and above all, his stature as the king of the jungle frightened the weak, fragile beast. Hearing his powerful roar, the fox became so scared that he fainted then and there. The next day, when he met the lion again, he was still afraid but gathered courage to conceal his fear. He left the place as soon as possible.

On the third day, the situation changed completely. The fox went up straight to the lion and said, "Hi Sir, hope everything is well." He started conversing with him as if he knew him for years. He was no longer afraid of the lion. Familiarity, thus, brings contempt.

11 The Foolish Cats

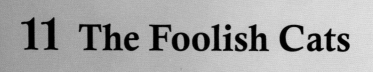

A cat saw a piece of bread on the road. But by the time it could reach it, another cat saw it and pounced on it. Both the cats started fighting.

After sometime, the cats decided to divide the bread into two pieces. But who would divide the piece of bread?

Meanwhile, a monkey came there. The cats asked the monkey to divide the bread into two halves.

The monkey was very cunning. He divided the bread into two pieces and checked their size. Finding one bigger than the other, he took a bite from the bigger piece. Then he noticed that the other piece was bigger and took a bite from that.

He carried on like this for some time and eventually, he ate up both the pieces, leaving the cats with nothing.

12 The Dog Who Went Abroad

Once there lived a dog called Chitranga, who was smart.

One year, a severe famine struck the town and Chitranga could not find anything to eat. So he ran away in desperation to a faraway land.

There was no shortage of food in this new land. He wandered into the backyard of a house where he ate to his heart's content and became a regular visitor there.

One day, some of the other local dogs spotted him. At once, they recognised that he was a stranger in their land and they attacked him.

Finally when he got away from them, he thought to himself, 'I had better leave from here if I want to stay alive. There may be a famine in my own land, but at least the dogs there are of my own kind and will accept me.'

13 The Story of the Blue Jackal

Once a jackal entered the house of a washerman and hid in a vat full of blue dye used for bleaching clothes. When he came out, he was dyed blue.

The jackal came back to the forest. All the animals got frightened on seeing him.

The jackal said, "There is no need to be afraid. I am a special creation of God. He nominated me as your king."

All the animals in the jungle accepted him as their king. They killed other animals and brought them as food for him.

One day, when the blue jackal was holding court, he heard a gang of jackals howling. Thrilled by the sound of his own ilk, he began responding loudly in his natural voice, and so it was revealed to all the other animals that he wasn't anything special; he was just a jackal who looked different.

14 The Vain Crows

A mynah wanted to fly to her nest as it was getting dark. Since her nest was far away, she stopped on a tree. Many crows were already perched on it.

On seeing the mynah, many crows shouted, "Get off our tree."

The mynah pleaded, "Let me stay for a while." But the crows wouldn't listen. At last, the mynah flew to another tree where she found a hollow to sit comfortably.

Later, it started raining heavily and hailstones fell. The mynah was safe inside the hollow. But many crows got hurt and some even died.

When the weather cleared, the mynah came out and flew homewards. One of the crows asked the mynah, "How come you are unhurt?"

"God helps humble creatures and lets arrogant ones like you suffer," the mynah said, and flew away.

15 A Bird in Hand

One day, the lion sighted a small rabbit frolicking under a nearby tree. The lion started stalking it, waiting for a chance to pounce on it. The rabbit saw the lion and ran for his life. But the lion sprang on it and the rabbit was in his paws. Before the lion could gobble up the rabbit, a deer came into the lion's view. The greedy lion let the rabbit go and ran after the deer.

The deer took long leaps to get away. The lion chased it, but the deer was too fast for him and disappeared into the forest.

The lion lost the rabbit and failed to hunt the deer as well. He cursed himself for letting go of the rabbit.

It is rightly said that a bird in hand is better than two in the bush.

16 The Flea and the Poor Bug

A bug lived in the linen spread over the king's bed. One day, the bug saw a flea drifting into the bedroom.

The flea said, "I have never tasted royal blood. It is not proper for you to siphon off the king's blood all alone. Share it with me also."

The bug told him, "You will have to wait till I finish my meal. After me, you can have your fill." The flea agreed.

Meanwhile, the king entered his bedroom. The impatient flea began feasting on the king's blood even before he went to sleep.

Stung by his bite, the king rose from his bed and asked his servants to look for what was on the bed. The king's men examined the bed closely.

The flea sneaked into a recess of the bed. The servants found the poor bug and killed him.

17 The Lion and the Clever Rabbit

Once upon a time, a mighty lion lived in a jungle. He roamed about freely, killing every creature that he came across. The animals were sad to see so many of them killed, and so they came to the lion and said, "You are our king. We want to spare you the trouble of hunting for your food, so we would like to send one animal from amongst us everyday to be your meal." The lion agreed and said, "But remember, one animal has to be at my doorway at lunch time every day or I will kill every single one of you."

After this, there was peace in the jungle. One day, a small, skinny rabbit was chosen to provide the lion's meal. He was clever and had made up his mind to save himself. He walked towards the lion's den, thinking of a plan. On the way,

he passed a deep old well and seeing his own reflection in the clear water, he had an idea. Meanwhile, the lion had come out of his den and roared angrily when he saw the rabbit.

The rabbit said, "Your Majesty, it's not my fault that I'm late, nor are the other animals to blame. Four rabbits were sent along with me to make a hearty meal for you. But on our way, a really big and powerful lion stopped us and demanded to know where we were going. When we told him, he got angry, and roared that he was the real king of the jungle, and that you are just an impostor. He pounced on the other four rabbits and said that they would make an excellent meal for him and sent me to you!"

The lion let out a deep roar of rage. "Who is this impostor who dares to challenge my position?" he exclaimed. "Lead me to him at once!"

The rabbit led the lion to the old well. "Look inside," he said, "and you will see the mighty lion yourself." The lion looked over the rim of the well, and as he looked into it, his own reflection stared back at him. Thinking that it was the impostor looking at him, he leapt into the deep well in rage, and drowned instantly. The clever little rabbit was saved.

Sometimes great strength is no match for a clever mind.

18 The Cunning Mediator

A sparrow made her home in the hollow of a big tree. One day, he left the tree in search of food. Meanwhile, a hare occupied the tree. When the sparrow returned, he discovered that the hare had occupied his hollow. The sparrow asked the hare to leave the tree, but the hare refused to leave.

They decided to go to a judge.

Meanwhile, a wicked cat came and pretended to be a wise judge.

Both of them approached the cat with their problem.

The cat said softly, "I am old and cannot see or hear very well. Come closer and narrate your story."

When the poor sparrow and hare came within the reach of the cat, he pounced on them and killed them both.

19 The Talking Cave

A lion lived in a jungle. One day, as he looked for a place to rest, he found a deep cave. He looked inside but did not find anyone inside it. He was sure that someone lived in the cave, but he liked it so much, that he wanted it for himself. Now the jackal that lived in this cave came back in the evening. He noticed the pugmarks of a lion leading to his cave. He was a clever jackal and decided to be careful. After all, he did not want to become a lion's dinner! The jackal, therefore, made a plan to confirm if the lion was inside the cave. He called out loudly, "O Cave! If you do not speak as usual, I will go away."

The lion decided to answer on behalf of the cave to lure the jackal in. So he roared out a greeting. Hearing this, the clever jackal ran away and saved his life.

20 The Monkeys and the Bell

Once, a group of monkeys found a bell in the jungle. Every night, the monkeys would enjoy the melodious sound of the bell. The villagers were afraid of the sound, believing it to be an evil spirit. An intelligent woman in the village went into the forest to find out the truth. She found that a group of monkeys were playing with the bell.

The woman put some groundnuts and fruits under a tree in the jungle and watched the monkeys from a distance.

The monkeys dropped the bell and ran to pick the eatables. The woman picked up the bell quickly and came back. The villagers praised her for her presence of mind.

One must not be afraid of trifles. Intelligence and courage succeed against all odds.

21 The Mouse Turned into a Lion

One day, a sage saw a mouse being chased by a cat. The sage, with his supernatural powers, turned him into a cat, to save his life. One day, a dog was chasing this cat. So, the sage turned him into a dog. Another day, the dog was attacked by a lion. This time, the sage immediately turned him into a lion.

The villagers who knew the lion's secret used to laugh at him. He was just a silly mouse pretending to be a lion! The lion thought he could never stop the jokes until and unless the sage died. So he went to kill the sage.

The sage, seeing the lion coming towards him, knew what was on his mind. And he said, "Go back to your form of a mouse, you are ungrateful and don't deserve to be a powerful lion."

And so the poor lion shrank back into a mouse.

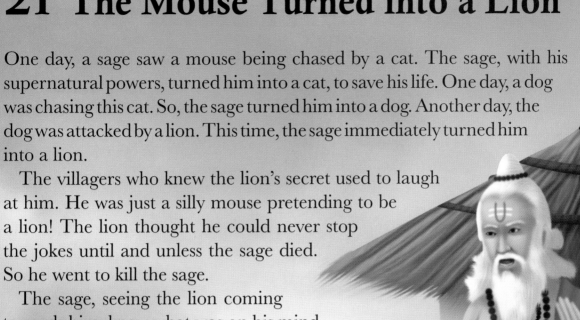

22 The Brahmin and the Goat

Once, long ago, there lived a brahmin. One day, while going home, he was carrying a goat on his shoulders. As he was walking along, two thieves spotted him. The thieves were part of a gang whose every move and action was well-coordinated and planned. When the thieves saw the goat with the brahmin, the first thing that came to their mind was to cheat the poor brahmin by taking his goat away. They could not have robbed him as it was daytime and they were on a very busy street. However, the thieves continued to pursue the brahmin, waiting to catch him at a lonely spot. The distance from the marketplace to his home was quite long. After walking some distance, the brahmin had to go through a stretch of forest to reach his home. The forest was lonely and the thieves thought that it would be the ideal place for them to cheat the brahmin. Their plan was ready now. The two thieves positioned themselves separately in the forest, so that no one would think that they were working together.

Their plan to trick the brahmin into parting with his goat was ready. They were only waiting for the right opportunity to implement it. As soon as the brahmin came into view, one of the thieves stepped into his path. With an expression of shock on his face, the thief said, "Why are you carrying such a dirty dog on your shoulders?"

The brahmin got angry. "Are you blind?" he snapped at the thief. "Can't you see that I am carrying a goat?" "I don't see a goat, I see a dog," said the thief. The brahmin looked at his goat carefully. He saw its face and features, and replied to the thief, "I am fairly confident that what I have is a goat and not a dog. Either you have not seen a goat before, or you have lost your mind. Whatever it is, let me have my goat and go my way." The brahmin continued to walk ahead, a little confused, when the second thief came and said, "Good heavens! Why are you carrying a dead calf on your shoulders, Sir?"

The brahmin was more confused this time. He lost faith in his own senses. 'What manner of beast am I carrying?' the brahmin thought in panic. 'Perhaps it is a demon that can change its form.' He threw the goat off his shoulders, and scampered away home. The thieves quickly grabbed the goat they wanted.

One should use one's own intelligence when judging any situation.

23 The Deer Who Played Truant

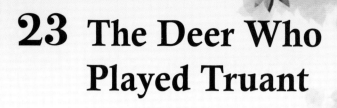

One day, a doe brought her son to a wise deer and told him, "O learned brother, please teach my little son the tricks to save himself from danger." The deer agreed. This little deer was very naughty and was interested only in playing with the other deer. Soon, he began missing classes and learnt nothing of self-defence. One day, while playing, he stepped on a snare and got trapped. When this bad news reached his mother, she broke into tears. The deer went up to her and said softly, "Dear sister, I feel sorry for what has happened to him. I tried my best to teach him self-defence. But he was not willing to learn. A teacher can't do anything if the student is not willing to learn."

24 The Magic Hen

One day, a poor man came up to a farmer and bought a sack of rice in exchange for a hen.

The farmer's wife was angry when she heard that her husband had parted with a whole sack of rice for an ordinary hen.

But the next morning, the farmer's wife found a golden egg at the place where the hen had roosted during the night.

The magic hen laid one golden egg everyday. This went on for several weeks. Soon the farmer became the richest man in the village.

But the farmer's wife, who was a greedy woman, was not satisfied. One day, when the farmer was not at home, she brought a big knife, and cut the hen's belly in the hope of getting all the golden eggs at once. To her dismay, she found that there was not even a single egg inside the hen! And there never would be any more eggs because the foolish, greedy woman had killed the magic hen.

25 The Donkey and the Washerman

Once, there lived a poor washerman who had a pet donkey. The donkey was very thin because he would get very little to eat.

One day, the washerman came across a dead tiger. He thought, 'I will put the tiger's skin on the donkey and let him graze in the neighbours' wheat fields at night. The farmers will mistake him for a tiger. The donkey can eat their crops throughout the night, as they would be too terrified to throw him out.'

The washerman immediately put his clever plan into action and it worked.

One night, while the donkey was busy eating in the field, he heard a female donkey braying at a distance. He became so excited that he couldn't help braying loudly in return.

Then the farmers came to know the truth and beat up the donkey severely!

It doesn't pay to pretend to be what you are not.

26 The Clever Farmer

Once, a farmer had a goat, a bundle of grass and a lion. He had to cross a river on a small boat, which could carry only two of them at a time. The farmer was in a fix. If he took the lion first, then the goat would eat up the grass in his absence. If he took the grass, the lion would eat up the goat.

At last, he found the perfect solution.

He first took the goat and left it on the other side of the river. Then, he took the lion on his second round. He left the lion and brought the goat back. Leaving the goat on this side, he took the bundle of grass. He left the grass with the lion and returned to take the goat in the end.

Thus, he crossed the river without any loss.

27 The Wise Minister

Once upon a time, a minister of a state invited the king to the wedding ceremony of his daughter. When the king arrived with the royal family, he guided him to the special seat arranged for the king. Once they reached the seat, the minister was embarrassed to find the sweeper sitting there. He pulled him up and scolded him publicly. The sweeper felt humiliated and planned to take revenge. Next morning, when he was sweeping the king's chamber, he deliberately muttered, "O the innocent king, I pity he does not know the juicy gossip about the minister and the queen." The king, who was half-asleep, sprang up. "What the hell are you saying?" asked he. "O sir, I had a sleepless night. I was in a daze," said the sweeper. But this was enough to put the seed of suspicion in the king's mind. After he left, the king said to himself, "The sweeper can be the most authentic source of such news. He visits all the rooms of the palace." The king started snubbing the minister. One day he even ordered the guards not to let him enter the palace. The minister was shocked but he guessed that the sweeper was responsible for it. 'I insulted him and he took revenge. Now I have to please him. Only he can repair

the damages he has caused in my life,' thought he. He one day gave the sweeper a cordial invitation at lunch and said, "My friend, please forgive me. I know I insulted you. But I did not realise it. Please take these silk clothes as gifts. Come and join me for lunch." The sweeper was pleased. He thought, 'The minister is always just. It was I who committed a mistake that day.' Now the sweeper was happy and he tried to make the king change his attitude towards the minister. He went to the king's chamber when he was sleeping, and muttered, "Oh. The king is having an affair with a housemaid. What a shame!" The king was disgusted to hear such a rumour. He woke up and loudly scolded the sweeper. The sweeper said, "Forgive me sir, I had a sleepless night. I was muttering in a daze." The king realised his mistake. Based on such rubbish mutterings, he had ignored his best advisor. The king called up the minister and they were friends again.

28 The Elephant and the Sparrow

One day, a wild elephant snapped the branch of a tree, crushing a sparrow's eggs in the nest. A woodpecker heard the female sparrow crying and asked her what had happened. She told him everything. The woodpecker said, "Let us consult the fly." They went to the fly and told him about the sparrow's grief. The fly suggested taking the frog's help. The sparrow, the woodpecker and the fly went to the frog and narrated everything.

The frog said, "What is an elephant before a united crowd like us? Do as I tell you. Oh fly, go to the elephant at noon and hum a sweet tune in his ears. When he closes his eyes in ecstasy, the woodpecker will scoop his eyes out. He will become blind and thirsty and will look for water. I will go to the quicksand and begin croaking there. Thinking that there is water, the elephant will come there and sink into the quicksand and die." All the four played out their roles according to the frog's plan and caused the death of the thoughtless elephant.

29 Unity is Strength

Once upon a time, there lived a flock of doves that flew from place to place in search of food, led by their king. One day, they were all trapped in a net. The doves desperately struggled to get out, but it was of no use.

The dove king had an idea. He told all the doves to fly up together at once, thus lifting the net along with them. The doves immediately obeyed their king. The hunter looked up in astonishment as he saw his net rise into the air with the flock of doves. The doves flew to the home of a mouse who was a faithful friend of the dove king. Eventually, the mouse chewed the net with his teeth and succeeded in freeing the doves.

30 The Frogs and the Snake

A snake made a plan to eat all the frogs of a lake. The snake said to the frogs, "I am here to serve you under a brahmin's curse." The frog king was thrilled and narrated this to all the frogs. All the frogs hopped on to the snake's back to take a ride.

The next day, the snake said, "I've had nothing to eat; I'm too weak to crawl swiftly." The frog king said, "You can eat the small frog at the end of your tail," which he did.

Over the next few days, the snake had eaten all the frogs except the frog king himself.

The next time the frog king said, "You may eat the frog at the end of your tail," the snake gulped him down.

31 The Two-Headed Weaver

One day, while a skilled weaver was weaving cloth; few pieces of his wooden loom broke apart. He took an axe, and set out to find some wood to replace them. He found a large tree and thought, 'If I cut down this tree, I will have enough wood to make all the tools I require for my weaving.' He raised his axe to begin chopping the tree. However, a spirit lived in the tree, and it called out, "This tree is my home, and I beg you to spare it." The weaver said, "I have no choice but to chop this tree down." The spirit requested, "I am a magic spirit. Why do you need to cut down this tree when I can reward you with anything you want? Ask for a boon and I shall grant it, if you spare this tree!" The weaver was extremely happy to learn that he could have his wishes fulfilled and the wildest of his desires granted by this magic spirit. But, showing extreme caution, the weaver said, "I'll have to talk to my wife about this. Wait, till I return." Then he hurried to consult his wife.

On the way, he met his friend and asked for his opinion. The friend said, "Don't waste away this opportunity. You should demand a kingdom. You could rule it as a king and enjoy a rich and princely life." The weaver apparently liked the idea suggested by his friend, yet showing extreme care and precaution before demanding his wish from the magic spirit, he said, "Let me take my wife's opinion too." He hurried to his wife and told her everything. The weaver's wife replied sharply, "Your friend has given you a foolish advice. Don't pay attention to it." She continued, "As a boon, you should ask for another pair of arms, and a second head, so that you can work on two pieces of cloth at the same time. Soon you'll be famous and rich, from the skill of your own hands!"

The foolish weaver said joyfully, "I will do exactly as you say. You are my wife and I am sure you have given me the best advice." The weaver went back to the spirit and demanded, "Give me another pair of arms and another head immediately." He had barely uttered the words before he had another head and an extra pair of arms too.

The weaver ran towards his house excitedly, but as he approached it, the local people screamed in terror mistaking him for a dreadful demon. They beat him till he fell down dead. The poor weaver perished because he mindlessly followed the advice of his wife.

45

32 The Swan and the Owl

Long ago, a swan lived by the side of a lake. An owl joined him there. They lived together happily. When the summer came, the owl thought of returning to his home. He asked the swan to join him. The swan said, "When the river goes dry, I'll come and join you." When the river went dry, the swan flew to the banyan tree where the owl lived. The swan went to sleep early.

Just then, a few travellers came to rest under the tree. Seeing the travellers, the owl hooted sharply. The travellers took it as a bad omen and one of them shot an arrow at the owl. As the owl could see in the dark, he escaped the arrow and flew away. The arrow pierced the swan instead and the poor thing died! It is rightly said, when in a new place, one must always stay alert.

33 The Bird with Two Heads

There lived a two-headed bird named Bharunda. One day, he found a golden fruit. One of the two heads started eating the fruit and found it very tasty. The other head said, "Let me also taste the fruit." The first head replied, "We've only one stomach, whichever head eats, the fruit will go to the same stomach." Later one day, the other head found a tree bearing poisonous fruits. He took the poisonous fruit and told the first head, "I will eat this poisonous fruit and take revenge." The first head yelled, "Please don't eat it. If you eat it, both of us will die." But the other head didn't bother and ate the poisonous fruit. Thus, both of them lost their lives.

34 The Wind and the Moon

A lion and a tiger lived together as friends. A monk also lived nearby. One day, the tiger said, "The cold comes when the moon decreases from full to new." The lion responded, "You are stupid, cold comes when the moon increases from new to full."

They decided to consult the monk for the correct answer.

The monk said, "It can be cold in any phase of the moon, from new to full and back to new again. It is the wind that brings the cold, whether from west or north or east. Therefore, both of you are right." The monk also said, "The most important thing is to live without conflict, to remain united." Both of them lived happily thereafter as good friends. Weather may change, but friendship remains.

35 The Dolphins and the Sprat

The dolphins and the whales were involved in a war with one another. When the battle was at its peak, a sprat stepped in and tried to reconcile them. However, the dolphins refused to accept any help from the sprat. Surprised, the sprat wanted to know the reason. To this, one of the dolphins cried out, "Stay away. We'll prefer death in the war to being reconciled by you—a small fish, so inferior to us!" The sprat felt bad and went away. The dolphins fought on and each of them was fatally wounded. Even when they were dying, there was pride on their faces. Pompous people can accept damage to any extent than avoid harm with the help of people from the lower rungs of society.

36 The Quails and the Hunter

There was once a quail hunter who hunted quails and their numbers were decreasing. One day, the king quail called for a meeting with all his subjects and said, "Tomorrow, when the hunter comes to catch us, we will all raise our heads in unison and fly away with the net to save our lives." The plan succeeded and the hunter couldn't catch even a single quail the following day. After a few days, the hunter returned. This time when he spread his net, the quails were trapped again. But, as they all got ready to fly, one quail accidentally stepped on the head of another. Both began to fight, forgetting all about the escape! The hunter caught them as they were unable to hold the net aloft for one another. In their hour of need, they all forgot about unity and therefore the hunter was successful in catching them.

37 The Birth of a Banyan Tree

Once there were three friends—a crow, a monkey and an elephant. Often, they had disagreements on many issues but failed to reach any conclusion. One day, they were resting under a big banyan tree when the monkey asked, "What was the size of the banyan tree when you first saw it?"

The elephant said, "As a baby, I used to rub my belly against its tender shoots."

"When I was young, I ate some berries and then dropped a few seeds here. This tree grew up from those seeds," the crow said solemnly.

Hearing him, the monkey said, "Friend, the first time I saw this tree it was a seedling. So, from now on, we shall listen to your opinions as you are oldest among us."

38 The Sage's Daughter

Once upon a time, there was a sage who lived with his wife on the banks of a river. The couple had no children of their own and longed to have one. One day, when the sage was engaged in penance, a kite dropped a she-mouse in the lap of the sage. The sage decided to bring her home, but he changed her into a girl before he did so.

On seeing the girl, the sage's wife asked, "Who is she? Where did you bring her from?" The sage told her all that had happened. His wife was very happy, and she exclaimed, "You have given her life and so, you are her father. That way, I am her mother. God must have sent her to us because we are childless."

Soon the girl grew into a beautiful maiden. When she was sixteen, the couple decided to get her married. The sage prayed to the Sun God to come to him. When the latter appeared, the sage asked him to marry his daughter.

However, the girl was not happy with the idea and said, "I am sorry, but I can't marry the Sun God, as he is burning hot." The disappointed sage then asked the Sun God himself to suggest a suitable groom for his daughter. The Sun God said, "The Lord of the Clouds could make a good match for her, as he is the only one who can protect her from the heat of the sun."

The sage then requested the Lord of the Clouds to marry his daughter. But the girl once again rejected the proposal, saying, "I don't want to marry a dark person like him. Besides, I am terrified of the thunder he sends out." The sage was disheartened again and asked the Lord of the Clouds to suggest a possible groom. The Lord of the Clouds said, "The Wind God can make a possible match for her as he can easily blow me away."

The sage then requested the Wind God to marry his daughter. This time too the girl declined the idea, saying, "I can't marry a frail person who is always blowing around." Deeply hurt and confused, the sage asked the Wind God to give his own suggestion. The Wind God replied, "The Lord of the Mountains is strong and stable and can stop the blowing wind easily. He would be a good choice."

The sage went to the Lord of the Mountains and asked him to marry his daughter. But the girl refused to accept him and said, "I can't marry someone who is too hard and cold." She asked the sage to find a softer husband for her. The sage sought the advice of the Lord of the Mountains. He replied, "A mouse will make a perfect match for her as he is soft and can easily make holes in any mountain."

This time the girl approved the idea. The sage was amazed and exclaimed, "How strange are the ways of destiny! You came to me as a mouse and I changed you into a human being. But being born a mouse you were destined to marry a mouse and fate has led you to this choice." He started praying and turned her back into a she-mouse. Destiny can never be changed.

39 The Mischievous Monkey

The Bodhisattva was once born as a hermit. Everyday, when he went to the village to seek alms, a monkey would enter his hut, eat all the food and do all sorts of mischief. Once the monkey came to the hermit's hut but found nothing to eat. So, he went to the village to look for the hermit. The villagers had just performed puja and were about to offer the prasad to the hermit. The monkey stood near the hermit, joining his hands as if he were in deep meditation. The villagers were pleased to see such devotion in a monkey. But the hermit recognised the mischievous monkey and told the villagers how the monkey troubled him every day. The angry villagers chased him away.

40 The Horse

Once upon a time, there lived a horse who owned a whole meadow. One day, when the horse was away, a stag came galloping in and damaged the entire pasture. When the horse came back, he found everything destroyed and was very angry.

He wanted to teach the stag a lesson, so he went to a man. "Can you please help me punish the wild stag?" asked the horse. The man said, "Yes. But tell me one thing. Will you let me climb your back and ride on you? Then I can punish the stag with a weapon in hand."

The horse said, "Why not? I'm ready."

Since then the horse, instead of taking revenge on the stag, is working as a slave of man.

41 How the Turtle Saved His Life

A king once built a pool for his young sons to play in. He ordered his men to put some fish into it. Quite by chance, the men also put in a turtle. The princes ran away in fright when they first saw it. The king ordered his men to kill the turtle. But they did not know how to. After much discussion, a guard said, "Throw it into the water where it flows out over the rocks into the river. Then, it will surely be killed." The turtle popped his head out of his shell and said, "You can throw me directly into the river in order to kill me!" The guards threw it into the water instead. The turtle laughed as he swam back home.

42 The Ass and Its Driver

An ass was being driven by his master. Suddenly, he broke free from the cart and ran frantically out of the trodden track. As he was running without direction, he ended up reaching a steep cliff. There was a deep valley below the cliff. Just when he was about to move a step forward, his master grabbed his tail and pulled him back. The ass also struggled to break free from the master. The master tried to drag him back with all his might. The master wanted to save the ass but the ass was blind to his fate. At last, the master let him go. "I quit. If you want to be your own master, I must let you go. A willful beast must go his own way." And so the ass jumped foolishly to his own end.

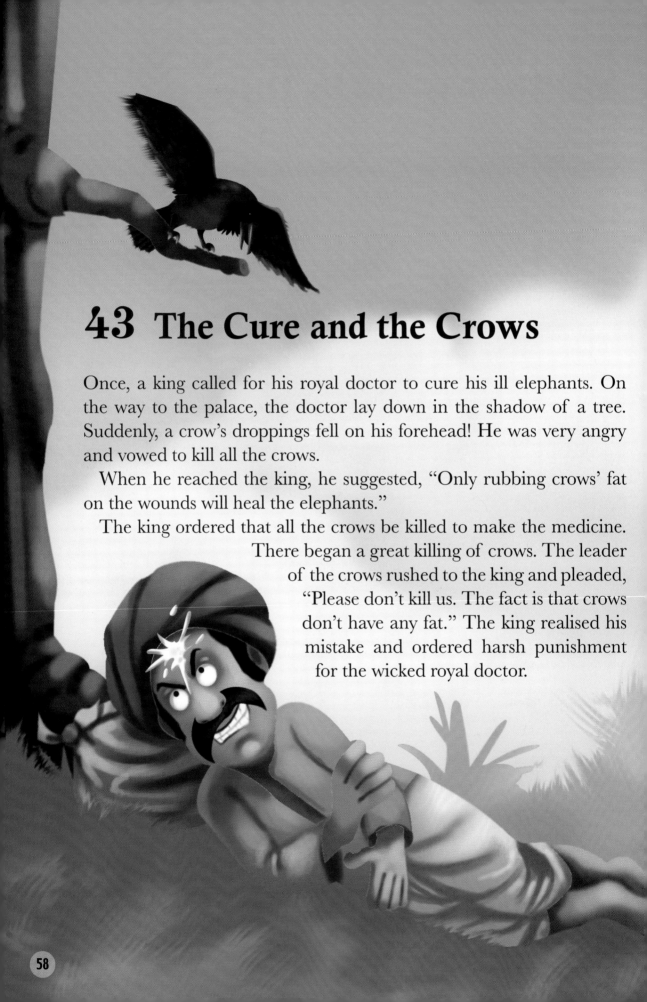

43 The Cure and the Crows

Once, a king called for his royal doctor to cure his ill elephants. On the way to the palace, the doctor lay down in the shadow of a tree. Suddenly, a crow's droppings fell on his forehead! He was very angry and vowed to kill all the crows.

When he reached the king, he suggested, "Only rubbing crows' fat on the wounds will heal the elephants."

The king ordered that all the crows be killed to make the medicine. There began a great killing of crows. The leader of the crows rushed to the king and pleaded, "Please don't kill us. The fact is that crows don't have any fat." The king realised his mistake and ordered harsh punishment for the wicked royal doctor.

44 The Mighty Fish

A long time ago, there lived a kind, pious fish. Suddenly, there was a terrible drought. The lake dried up and many water creatures lost their lives. Seeing the great danger they were all facing, the pious fish decided to do something to save himself and the others.

One day, ignoring all risks, the pious fish made his way through the mud and came up to the surface. There he called upon the Rain God and prayed, "O lord! Pardon our sins. Please send rain and relieve us from this misery."

Such was his cry that it shook everything from hell to heaven and God's heart filled with compassion. He sent heavy rains to the earth and thus the great fish and his companions were saved.

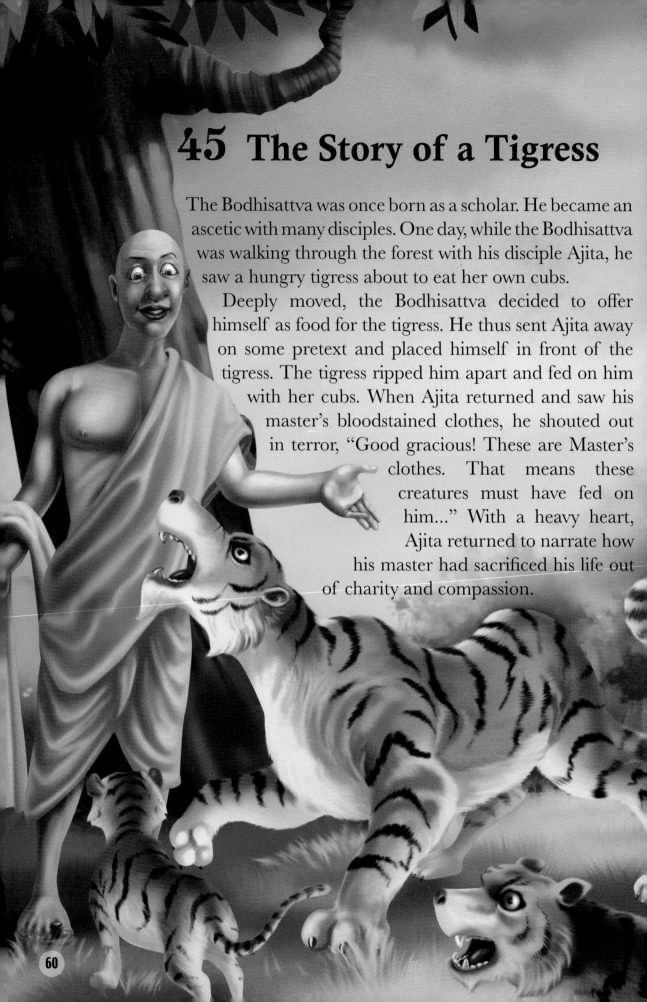

45 The Story of a Tigress

The Bodhisattva was once born as a scholar. He became an ascetic with many disciples. One day, while the Bodhisattva was walking through the forest with his disciple Ajita, he saw a hungry tigress about to eat her own cubs.

Deeply moved, the Bodhisattva decided to offer himself as food for the tigress. He thus sent Ajita away on some pretext and placed himself in front of the tigress. The tigress ripped him apart and fed on him with her cubs. When Ajita returned and saw his master's bloodstained clothes, he shouted out in terror, "Good gracious! These are Master's clothes. That means these creatures must have fed on him..." With a heavy heart, Ajita returned to narrate how his master had sacrificed his life out of charity and compassion.

46 The Selfish Swans

In a palace, lived a kind-hearted king. There was a pond in the palace which was home to golden-coloured swans. They led a luxurious life. They used to give the king their golden feather each month. One day, there came a migratory bird. The swans became jealous of it. "See the bird is pure golden in colour. He is bound to get preference. We must chase the bird away if we need to remain important," they said to one another.

Suddenly, the king's men saw the swans attacking the bird. The king rushed out of the palace and saw the violent scene.

"Catch those swans and cage them. They are now jealous of the guest bird," the king said angrily.

The swans flew away from the vicinity. Jealousy robbed them of all they had.

47 The Tale of the Two Cats

A poor old woman once lived in a hut with a small thin cat. The cat lived on the measly leftovers and thin watery gruel that the old woman occasionally gave him.

One morning, the thin cat saw a fat cat walking along the wall of the opposite house. The thin cat called out to him, "My dear friend, it seems you get to feast everyday at a banquet. Pray, tell me where you find so much food."

The fat cat said, "At the king's table, of course. Every day, before the king sits down to eat, I hide under the table and steal the tasty pieces that drop from it."

The thin cat let out a long sigh of longing, and the fat cat said, "I can take you to the king's palace tomorrow. But remember, once we are there, you will have to fend for yourself."

"Oh thank you!" purred the thin cat joyfully, and he ran to tell his mistress.

The old woman was far from happy to hear him. "I beg you," she pleaded with her cat, "stay at home and be content with your gruel. What will happen if the royal servants catch you stealing?"

But the thin cat was so greedy that he paid no heed, and the two cats started for the palace jauntily.

Now it had so happened that the day before, cats had invaded the king's banquet hall in such large numbers that the angry king had issued an order that any cat entering the palace gates would be put to death instantly. As the fat cat was creeping in through the gate, another cat, who was fleeing, warned him of the king's orders. The fat cat immediately turned and ran away.

But the thin cat was already close to the banquet hall. In a frenzy of excitement, he leapt through the window and was just snatching a piece of fish from a serving bowl, when a royal servant seized and killed him.

48 The Arab and the Camel

A man was once about to set out for a long journey across the Arabian Desert. Before leaving, he spent quite some time preparing his luggage. Thereafter, he loaded all he wanted to take with him on the back of the camel. When the preparations for the journey were over, he asked the camel whether he would prefer going uphill or downhill. The camel listened to him carefully and calculated the weight put on him. After a while, the camel asked his master, "Sir, is there a third option of undertaking a journey straight across the plain? If it is possible, then I'll be happy to take that route. Given the weight of the luggage I am carrying, I think the easiest route should be preferred."

49 The Peacock and the Crane

There lived a peacock beside a lake. He had beautiful feathers that he admired. One day, a crane came to stay there. The peacock said, "I am glad to welcome you to this place." Now, the peacock spread its feathers. The colourful feathers looked beautiful in the bright sunlight. It reflected in the water of the lake.

The proud peacock said, "Look at my feathers. They are so beautiful and special. Far more beautiful than yours." The crane understood the tone.

He said, "Whatever I have, I can fly with it. Your beauty is useless because your feathers don't help you to fly." The curt remark brought the peacock down to ground. It made him humble.

50 The Fox and the Grapes

A hungry fox was roaming in the jungle. Suddenly, he came across a place where ripe, juicy grapes hung high on the vines. He said to himself, "These must be tasty. I should eat them." The grapes hung higher than he could reach. So he jumped high to try to reach those fruits but in vain. He kept jumping high to gain access to the juicy, ripe bunch but he failed each time. He tried again and again but failed everytime. When he got tired and realised that he had to give up, he retreated and said to himself, "O! I really don't need those grapes. Those were sour." The behaviour of the fox shows that one finds it easy to despise the thing that one cannot get.

51 The Crooked Eagle

Once, an eagle lived on the branch of a tree, while a fox lived in the hole of the same tree.

One day, when the fox left the hole, the eagle went down to the hole and took the fox-cubs to feed his offspring. When the fox returned home, he pleaded to the eagle to return the cubs. Thinking that his nest was too high for the fox to reach, the eagle ignored his request. The fox went to a temple nearby and brought a fire-lit torch. He immediately set the tree on fire. The heat and the smoke frightened the eagle. For the safety of his own kids, he flew down to the fox and returned him his cubs. It is true that a tyrant is never safe from the ones he oppresses.

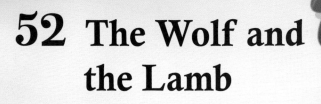

52 The Wolf and the Lamb

A wolf saw a lamb and planned to eat him. They were standing by a small river. The wolf said to the lamb, "How dare you dirty the water I am drinking?" "The stream is flowing from your side," said the innocent lamb. "Okay!" said the wolf, adding, "But how will you explain your bad conduct last year? I heard you calling me names openly." Taken aback, the poor beast said, "I was not even born then." "Oh," the wolf made a small revision in his statement, and said, "then it would have been your mother. Be punished for the crime committed by your mother." Wasting no time, the wolf killed the lamb. A tyrant, always finds its excuse and those who are oppressed can never beat them in argument.

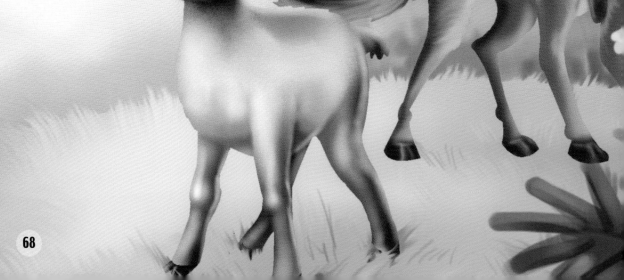

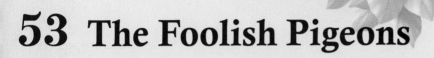

53 The Foolish Pigeons

Once upon a time, there was a hungry hawk that chased a flock of pigeons, who always managed to fly to safety. The pigeons remained scared of the hawk, always alert to the possible attacks of the fierce bird. The desperate hawk, who wanted to prey on them for a long time, hit on a plan and went to the pigeons, saying, "What's the use of leading such a life in fear? Better make me the king of your clan so that I can protect you against dangers."

The pigeons felt inspired. They thought the hawk is interested in their welfare. They made the hawk their king.

Immediately after becoming their leader, the hawk started eating the pigeons one by one.

Some remedies are worse than dangers.

54 The Leopard and the Fox

A leopard and a fox lived together in a jungle. They were good friends and had never had any quarrel on trifles and petty issues. However, one day, it so happened that they had a heated discussion which eventually culminated in a contest to decide who was more handsome of the two. The leopard first insisted that he was more handsome as he had an unusual, bright yellow coloured body. He boasted of his innumerable black spots. The fox listened to him attentively and agreed. Then, after a brief pause, he said, "Yes, you are more beautiful than me. You have a spotted body and it's bright in colour. But I think my smart mind is more important than your beautiful body."

55 The Lion and the Three Bulls

Once upon a time, there were three bulls. They were very good friends. They grazed together and shared everything among themselves without malice or grudge. A lion had long been eyeing them for prey, but he knew as long as they were together, he could not match their collective strength. So he hit a cunning plan to separate them from each other. He started spreading rumours about the bulls. The false rumours bred misunderstanding among them. Slowly and slowly they grew jealous of one another. And finally this resulted in disharmony and they started living separately. It was a golden opportunity for the lion and he did not waste it. He killed them one by one and ate them. Unity is strength.

56 The Story of the Merchant's Son

A merchant's son purchased a book for Rs100. It had just one sentence, 'Man gets what he is destined to.' The merchant was annoyed at his foolishness and threw him out of his house. The poor boy went to another city and began a new life under the name Prapta.

Chandravati, the princess of the city, loved a handsome warrior and asked her maid to arrange a meeting with him. The maid secretly invited the warrior to the palace that night. She asked him to climb the palace wall with the help of a rope that would be hanging there.

The warrior, however, was not interested in meeting the princess and never turned up. Meanwhile, Prapta noticed the suspended rope, climbed the wall and found himself in the princess' bedroom.

The princess, mistaking him for the warrior, said to him, "O handsome soldier, I have fallen in love with you." To this Prapta replied, "Man gets what he is destined to."

The princess realised this man was not the one she was expecting, and she asked him to go away. Prapta left the palace and went to sleep at a temple. But the Mayor of the city had come to hold a secret meeting there and told Prapta to sleep at his house.

When Prapta reached the Mayor's house, his daughter Vinayawati mistook him for her prospective husband and made arrangements to marry him. Before tying the knot, Vinayawati asked Prapta to say something, and he recited his usual sentence about destiny. His words annoyed her and she asked him to leave at once.

Prapta once again took to the street. His eyes fell on a marriage procession in which an elephant had gone berserk and was charging at everyone. The bridegroom and his party soon fled the scene of marriage.

Prapta saw that the frightened bride was alone. He came forward and drove away the elephant courageously. Meanwhile, as peace returned, the bride's father, a merchant, along with the marriage party, came back to the venue. The daughter told her father, "This brave man saved me from the mad elephant. I won't marry anyone but him."

Hearing the commotion, the princess and the king came to the wedding venue to see what had happened, and so did the Mayor's daughter. The king asked Prapta to tell him everything without fear. Prapta as usual repeated the same sentence.

The sentence rang a bell in the princess' head. The Mayor's daughter was also reminded of her meeting with Prapta. The king, the Mayor, and the merchant, all three married off their daughters to Prapta and the king gave him a thousand villages as a wedding gift. Everyone agreed that even God cannot undo what is destined for man.

57 The Foolish Crow

A hawk once lived on the top of a hill. In the valley, a crow had made its nest on a banyan tree. The crow was foolish and lazy and never wanted to work hard to hunt for food. He wished to feed on the rabbits, which lived in a hole under the same tree. The hawk used to hunt the rabbits occasionally by swooping down on them from above.

The crow's mouth watered at the thought of eating tasty rabbit meat. One day, he decided that he must hunt like a hawk in order to catch a rabbit. So the next day, the crow flew very high in the sky and then came down in a fast swoop after spotting a rabbit. But there cannot be a comparison between a hawk and a crow. The rabbit had noticed the crow and hid behind a rock. The crow came down blindly and dashed against the rock and died on the spot.

One must not blindly copy others, but must keep in mind one's own capacity and skills.

58 The Handsome Camel

One day, a poor villager discovered three camels—two kids and their mother. He took them to his home and started to look after them. He used to take them to the forest for grazing and to the river for bathing. He thought, 'Let these camels grow, they will mate and I'll possess many more camels. Then I'll become a camel trader. Our poverty will come to an end.' Whenever he used to ride the camels, his neighbours envied him. In some years, he had several camels. He became rich. Other villagers were jealous of him. One day, one of his jealous neighbours asked him, "How will you know which one is roaming where unless you tie a bell on the neck of one?" The carpenter tied a bell to the neck of one of the camels. One day, the camel with the bell was roaming in the jungle. His bell tinkled continuously. A tiger heard the bell and pounced at him and made him his food. Thus, the carpenter suffered the loss as he blindly trusted a jealous neighbour.

59 The Crab and His Mother

One early morning, the mother crab took her son for a stroll along the beach. While he was walking, the mother asked, "Oh, my son, why do you walk sideways like that with your toes turned in?" The young crab said, "Can you please show me?" Mother crab was very glad to hear that her son was willing to learn. "I will show you, my son. Now step back and watch carefully," said the mother crab. With that, the mother crab stretched out one of her legs, turned her toes out and tried to take a step forward. But as soon as she did that, she tripped and fell flat on her nose! Do not tell others how to act unless you can set a good example.

60 The Cock Who Found a Jewel

Once, a cock felt hungry and went in search of food. He started scratching the ground in hope of finding grains for his meal. Meanwhile, he discovered a jewel deep in the mud. It was precious and big. The cock was surprised to see it. He lifted it and said to himself, "What a pretty jewel it is! It must be very precious. The world will run after it." After sometime he thought, "I am hungry and I need food. What will I do with a jewel? At this time, a grain is more precious to me because I can eat it. So the jewel is meaningless to me." He left the jewel there and started digging at another place. Actually, a thing is precious only if it is useful to you.

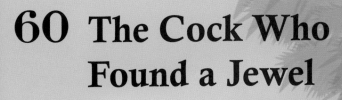

61 The Wise Fox

A hungry fox was roaming the forest when he saw a dead elephant. He jumped on it to have his fill, but his teeth could not penetrate the thick skin of the animal. He thought he would persuade a sharp-toothed beast to eat the elephant and then have the remaining flesh after he had had his share.

So he went to a lion and said, "Sir, I have killed an elephant. Come, feast on it, my lord." The invitation made the lion angry. "I don't touch the flesh of the animal I have not killed," he growled.

The poor fox then went to a tiger and said, "Sir, the lion has just killed an elephant. Now he has gone to take a bath, and I am guarding the flesh. Please come and enjoy it." But the tiger showed no interest and went away.

Finally, the fox approached a wolf and he agreed. As the wolf was eating, the lion happened to pass by. On seeing the lion, the wolf ran away. The fox, who had never really wanted to share his meal with anyone, happily ate the elephant.

62 Shani, Mangal and Shukra

The planet gods Shani, Mangal and Shukra decided to find which one of them could make a perfect thing. Shani made a man. Mangal made a bull and Shukra made a house. They called Lord Narada to judge which of them is perfect. Narada started with the bull and found fault with its horns above his eyes. "This," he said, "does not enable the bull to see his own horns." The man, according to him, was faulty because he did not have windows in his chest so that his inward thoughts may come out. The house, lastly, was criticised as it lacked wheels and was not mobile. Listening to this, Shani said, "A fault-finder like you is never pleased. Stop criticising others until you have made something worthwhile yourself."

63 The Wild Boar and the Fox

A wild boar was whetting his tusks against a tree trunk. A fox saw him and wondered why the silly creature was preparing for a fight when there was no danger around. So he went up to the boar and asked, "Why are you whetting your tusks, dear friend? Look around. Is there any hunter or fierce animal? In fact, there is no danger at all. So I think what you are doing is totally useless."

The boar looked at him and remarked patiently, "O my dear friend! When danger arrives, it arrives suddenly. And when it comes, I may have something else in mind instead of whetting my tusks. As you know, it's too late to whet the sword when the trumpet for war blows."

64 The Foolish Raven

Once a raven saw a swan and, being all black himself, he was impressed with the bird's beautiful white colour. He longed to be as fair as the swan and thought if he lived in a pond like the swans do, he would become white too. So he left his usual haunt where he used to find his daily food and flew down to the pond. He plumed himself and washed his coat again and again. But all his efforts went in vain. His feathers remained as dark as they always were. The poor raven was doubly disappointed as he could not find his usual food in the new place. He soon died of hunger and grief.

Changing one's place of stay does not change one's nature.

65 The Foolish Goat

One day, a fox fell into a deep well. Soon a goat came to the same well to take a drink. He was amazed to see a fox swimming in the water. The fox thought he must use the goat to rescue himself. He cried, "Hey, goat! Do you know why I am down in here? It's easiest to get all the good water if you are inside the well. Look! I am drinking and enjoying to my heart's content."

The fox's words tempted the goat, and he soon jumped into the well. The fox immediately caught hold of the goat, climbed onto his back, and after a little effort, managed to leap out of the well. The poor goat was almost drowning, and he cried out for help. The fox said, "You are a fool. Always look before you leap. Now that you have broken the golden rule, you deserve to suffer."

66 The Crow Who Wanted to be a Peacock

A crow gathered together some peacock feathers one day and stuck them all over his body. He was very proud of his new look and thought he should be living with peacocks instead of crows. So he scoffed at his old friends and went and tried to mingle with a group of peacocks. However, the peacocks noticed in no time that there was a crow among them. They stripped him of all his colourful plumes, pecked at him and made fun of him. The bitter and battered crow returned home with a heavy heart. His fellow crows shook their heads and said, "You are a wretched creature! Had you been satisfied with your own feathers, you would never have had to face the taunts of your superiors or the hatred of your equals."

67 The Lion and the Fox

A lion, a fox and an ass went out for hunting. As they roamed the forest, they came across a big stag. Together they gave it a chase, killed it and then decided to divide the meal. The ass came forward and divided the heap of flesh into three portions. The lion, however, was furious as he wanted the biggest share. He pounced on the ass and killed him instantly. Then the lion asked the fox to divide the meat. The fox was wise. He gathered every piece in a heap, separated a tiny amount from it and set it aside for himself. The lion, quite amused, asked him, "Who taught you this art of division?"

The fox wittily replied, "Sir, the ass's fate!"

It is better to learn from the mistakes of others than from your own.

68 The Sandy Road

One day, a merchant decided to go to the town to try his fortune. He arranged for some men who could go along with him. They had to cross a desert to reach the town.

When they reached the desert, it was very hot. So, the merchant and his people waited for the night to resume their journey. As night fell, they resumed their journey. One of them had some knowledge of the stars. So, he was guiding the way for other people by reading the position of stars. They travelled for the whole night without taking any break. At daybreak, they stopped and camped.

After travelling for two days, they found that it was just one more day's journey, after which they would arrive at the town. Suddenly, they found that there was no water left with them. Every one was tired and had no energy left to continue travelling without water. So they sat down. The merchant decided to find water. He walked down. Finally, he saw some grass and thought, 'There

must be water somewhere below, otherwise, that grass would not be there.'

All of them ran with the merchant and started digging. The merchant jumped down into the hole they had dug and kept his ear to the rock. He called to them, "I can hear water running under this rock. We must not give up." Then, the merchant came out of the hole and said to the serving boy, "My boy, if you give up, we are lost. Please go down and try."

The boy stood up raising the hammer high above his head and hit the rock with his full strength. He didn't give up, reminding himself of the merchant's words. Ultimately, the rock broke and the hole was full of water. All the men drank water, as if they could never get enough. They watered the oxen and bathed.

After drinking and bathing, they split the extra wooden yokes and axles from their carts. They made a fire out of it and cooked rice. They had their meal and rested through the day. They also placed a flag on the well, so that passing travellers could see it from a distance. After sunset, they started their journey and reached the town in the morning. They sold the goods making huge profits and happily returned to their village.

Will and Determination can achieve anything.

69 The Pig and the Sheep

There was a fat and healthy pig who was always scared that he might be caught and slaughtered any time. He took shelter in the sheepfold, thinking it might help him avoid notice and escape the slaughterhouse. One day, the shepherd saw him and grabbed him by his ear. The pig screamed and struggled with all his might to free himself from the man's clutches. A sheep who stood watching close by asked him to relax. "Why are you panicking? Our master does this often with us, but we don't cry like you. Stop the commotion," they said.

The pig replied, "My friend, my case is different. He catches hold of you to check or shear the wool. But men catch us to have delicious dinner."

70 The Hunter and the Rabbit

Once, a cruel hunter used to catch rabbits and feast upon their meat. One day, he caught a rabbit and holding him by his ears, started for home. On the way home, the hunter met a saint. The saint asked the hunter to free the rabbit and get blessed for the good deed.

The hunter not only refused but decided to cut the throat of the rabbit then and there mercilessly, right before the saint.

He took out a sharp knife from his bag, but when he tried to cut the rabbit's neck, the knife slipped from his hand and fell on his foot, severely injuring him. He instantly cried out in pain and released the rabbit.

The hunter paid the price for his sins. Since his foot was very badly injured, he could not walk properly and became unfit to hunt ever again.

71 The Greedy Little Bird

Long ago, on a hot summer day, the king of birds, along with other birds, flew to a new place in search of food. He asked them to begin searching in all directions.

All the birds flew far and wide in search of food. One of the birds reached a highway. There she saw many bullock carts carrying sacks of food grains. She also noticed that lots of grains were falling on the road as the carts moved.

She was delighted and decided to tell the king about this place before anyone else found it. So she flew back and said to the king of birds, "I saw a place where many sack-laden bullock carts pass by on the road and spill grains. But if you fly down on that road to peck at the grain, the carts may crush you at any time. It's better not to go there at all."

The bird's advice seemed sensible and the king agreed. He warned the other birds not to go anywhere near the highway.

The little bird would secretly fly to the spot everyday and enjoy the feast alone. One day, while she was pecking at the grains, a bullock cart came and crushed the greedy bird.

72 The Lion and the Mouse

It was a warm day and a lion was taking a nap in his cave. Suddenly a mouse ran over his nose by mistake and awakened the great beast. The lion was about to crush the mouse under his paws, when the little creature started begging for his life. The lion took pity on the mouse and let it go. A few days later, the lion, while wandering in the forest, stepped into a trap set by hunters and was caught in the nets. He was so tightly entangled in ropes that he could hardly move. The lion lay on the ground and roared helplessly. His cries echoed across the forest and reached the mouse's ears. He rushed to the spot and bit the threads of the net into pieces.

At times even the small and the weak turn out to be mightier than most.

73 The Lion and the Wolf

Once upon a time, a wolf killed a sheep and was about to carry the corpse to his den. Suddenly, a lion pounced forward and tried to snatch the sheep away. The wolf looked at the lion and shouted, "You should be ashamed of yourself. You are the king of the forest, and you know everyone trusts you. How can you rob me of my food? You are a disgrace to the forest!"

The lion laughed at the wolf and said, "Why should I be ashamed of myself? I have robbed someone who is a rogue himself and steals all the time. How dare you accuse me in this way, you wily beast. It is you who should be ashamed in the first place for having robbed the shepherd of his sheep."

One thief is no better than the other.

93

74 Tale of Two Friends

In a city, there lived two friends named Dharmabuddhi and Papabuddhi.

Cunning Papabuddhi planned to deprive Dharmabuddhi of all his wealth. He told Dharmabuddhi, "Dear friend, I strongly feel it is not safe to keep all our wealth at home. We should bury our money in some secret place in a forest. Whenever we need money, we can go there and get it."

Dharmabuddhi agreed, and they dug a pit deep inside a

nearby forest and buried their earnings in it. One night, Papabuddhi went to the pit and stole all the money. Next morning, he went to Dharmabuddhi and asked him to accompany him to the forest because he needed money.

When both of them arrived at the pit and found it empty, Papabuddhi began shouting loudly, "Dharmabuddhi, you stole the money. You must give me half of what was buried here." Though Dharmabuddhi denied it vehemently, Papabuddhi persisted in his accusations.

The case was brought to the court. There, Papabuddhi said to the judge, "I can produce the gods of the forest as witnesses. They will determine who is guilty." The judges agreed and asked both parties to be present the next morning at the forest.

Papabuddhi went home and told his father, "Father, I have stolen all of Dharmabuddhi's money. There is a court case going on, and I can win it only with your help. Go now and hide in the hollow of the big tree in the forest. Tomorrow morning, when the judges and others assemble there, I will ask you for the truth. Then you say that Dharmabuddhi is the thief."

The father hesitated to lend support to the wicked plan, but finally he agreed as he loved his son.

The next day, while Dharmabuddhi and the judges watched, Papabuddhi went near the tree and shouted, "O gods of the forest, you are all witnesses. Declare who among us is guilty."

The father shouted back from inside the hollow of the tree, "It is Dharmabuddhi who stole the money."

Dharmabuddhi felt suspicious. He filled the tree hollow with hay, poured oil on it and threw a matchstick in. The fire forced the father to come out of the tree.

"All this is the work of Papabuddhi's evil mind," said the father to the judges. The king's men arrested Papabuddhi.

75 The Woodcutter and the Fox

A fox, chased by hunters, rushed to a woodcutter and begged for shelter. The woodcutter pointed his finger at his hut and the fox took refuge there. The hunters soon came up and asked, "Have you seen a fox around?"

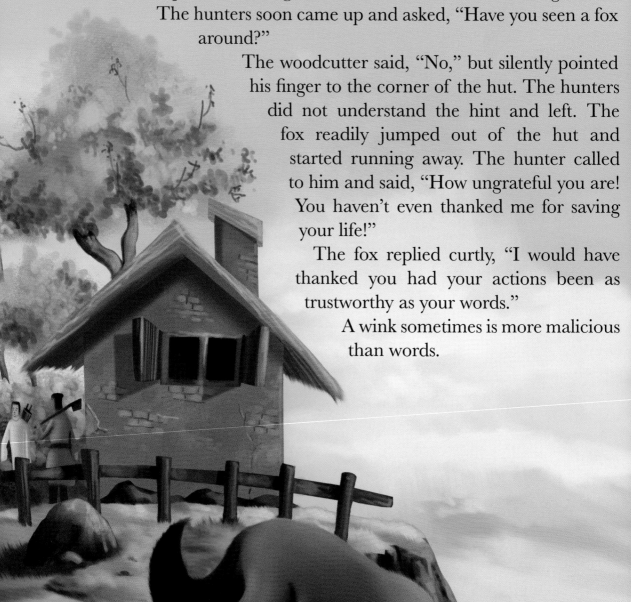

The woodcutter said, "No," but silently pointed his finger to the corner of the hut. The hunters did not understand the hint and left. The fox readily jumped out of the hut and started running away. The hunter called to him and said, "How ungrateful you are! You haven't even thanked me for saving your life!"

The fox replied curtly, "I would have thanked you had your actions been as trustworthy as your words."

A wink sometimes is more malicious than words.

76 The Monkey and the Camel

Many years ago, all the animals of the forest assembled together in a show of their histrionic talents. As the audience waited, the monkey was asked to dance. Known for his natural acrobatic skills, the monkey delighted everyone with his moves. There was a huge applause and the monkey was hailed as a great dancer. The camel could not stand the monkey being praised. He jumped up and started dancing too. But his performance had neither rhythm nor grace and he ended up making a fool of himself. As a punishment for his jealousy, he was banished from the land.

If you stretch your arms beyond your sleeves, you are bound to suffer.

77 The Rivers and the Sea

Since old times, the rivers and the seas lived in perfect harmony. The rivers would pour all their water into the sea, and the sea would happily accept it so that the rivers remained clean and safe. The rivers, however, were not happy with the fact that the sea turned all the water salty. One day, they decided to make a complaint. They joined together and moved towards the sea. When they reached the vast blue expanse, they all asked in one voice, "O sea, why is it that you always make salty the sweet water we pour into you everyday?"

The sea remained unmoved by the collective anger and replied calmly, "If you do not wish to become salty, keep away from me."

The rivers returned crestfallen, as they knew they could not do without the sea.

78 The Old Tiger and the Greedy Traveller

An old tiger found he no longer had the strength to hunt for food. Holding a golden bracelet, he stood in the mud and started shouting, "Look, everyone! Come and take this beautiful piece of gold jewellery."

A passerby felt tempted, but was also scared to approach a tiger. "How can I trust you?" he asked from a safe distance. "You may eat me up if I try to take that bracelet."

The tiger replied, "I used to kill others. But now I lead a pious life and enjoy giving." The traveller came up to the tiger, but he got stuck in the mud. The old tiger had been waiting for this moment. He pounced on him and started dragging him through the mud. The man lamented, "Oh poor me! In my greed, I forgot the simple rule that a killer always remains a killer."

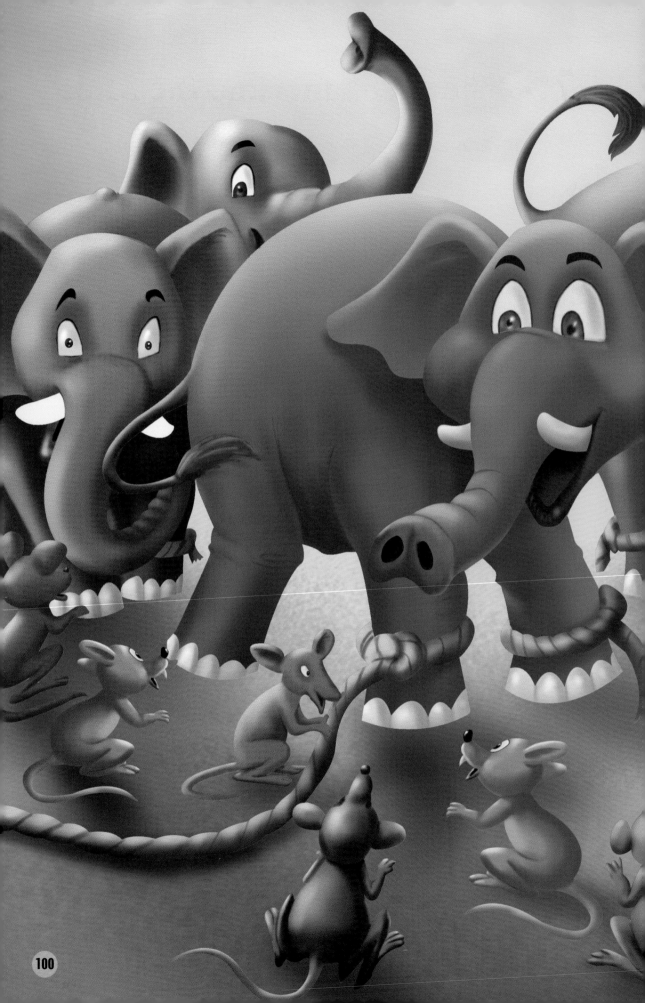

79 The Elephants and the Mice

Once, a group of mice lived in a palace they made beside a deep lake.

One day, a herd of elephants while going towards the lake, ran over hundreds of little mice.

The mice that survived were worried. The leader of the mice said, "We should appeal to their kindness."

The mice requested the leader of the elephant herd. "Your herd stomped through our home on the way to the lake, killing hundreds of mice. We beg you to take another route."

The elephant leader agreed.

One day, the king ordered to trap all the elephants. The traps were laid in the forest. All the elephants except for one were caught in the traps. Then, the elephant that escaped the traps went to the leader of the mice and requested for their help. All the mice hurried towards the trapped elephants and began to chew off the thick ropes with their sharp teeth, freeing all the elephants. Kindness is always returned with more kindness.

80 The Frog and the Mouse

A wicked frog once made friends with a mouse. One day, they set out on a long journey. On the way, they came across a pond. The mouse was scared of entering the water, but the frog assured the mouse he would help him cross the pond. He tied the legs of the mouse with his own legs and took a plunge in the water. As the frog reached the middle of the pond, where the water was deepest, he started dragging the mouse below the water. The mouse struggled hard to free himself, and their tussle created a huge commotion in the water. The disturbance attracted the attention of a hawk hovering over the pond. It flew down, snatched up the mouse in its talons and flew away. The treacherous frog suffered along with the mouse as his legs were tied to the mouse and he was taken away too.

Those who harm others often become victims of their own actions.

81 The Peach and the Apple

One day, a peach and an apple were having an argument in an orchard. Each was trying to prove that he was more beautiful than the other. As none seemed to win, they decided to settle the issue through an open debate. A loud exchange of words began again between the two fruits while other fruits listened. A blackberry in the nearby bush thrust its head out and cried, "Your dispute has gone on long enough and does not seem to settle. There is nothing that you will gain from it. So forget your differences, shake hands and be friends again. This is the only way to live in peace."

Loudest quarrels are often the pettiest ones.

82 The Sun's Marriage

It was a hot summer day when all the creatures of the earth got to hear a rumour that the sun was soon going to tie the nuptial knot. They were all beside themselves with joy. The frogs too were overjoyed and celebrated the happy news with umpteen leaps in the water. An old toad came up with a serious face and reminded them that it was an occasion of sorrow rather than of joy, "My friends! Why are you so happy? Is the news really something we should be celebrating? A single sun scorches us with such blazing heat. Think of the time when there will be a dozen kids of the sun. Our sufferings will increase, and we may not survive at all."

83 The Farmer and the Fox

There was once a fox, who always troubled a farmer by eating up his hens from the poultry farm. The farmer was really fed up and decided to teach the fox a lesson. After many days, he finally caught the fox.

In his anger, he picked up a length of rope and soaked it with oil. He then tied the rope to the fox's tail and set it on fire.

But it was not only the fox that was harmed. The fox ran into the farmer's crops with its burning tail. Soon all the crops caught fire and were destroyed! If only the farmer had not acted out of anger, he would not have had to suffer such a big loss. He was very sorry to have lost his temper and vowed never to act out of anger again.

84 The King Who Knew the Language of Animals

Once, a king saved the life of a serpent. The pleased serpent in return gifted him the power to understand the language of animals provided he kept it a secret. If he revealed the secret, he would have to die.

One day, when he was sitting with his queen in the garden, he heard an ant speak about a piece of sweet and he smiled as he listened. The queen pressed him to tell her the reason of his smile despite the king explaining to her the consequences. The king was about to reveal his secret. Suddenly, a heavenly voice said, "O king, why should you sacrifice your life for someone who doesn't value yours?"

The king then accused his wife of being selfish. The queen realised her mistake.

85 The Boy Who Cried Wolf

Long ago, there was a shepherd boy who used to take his flock of sheep to the forest. One day, he decided to play a trick on the villagers. He shouted, "Help! Wolf!"

The villagers heard his cries and came rushing. When they reached the boy, they saw there was no wolf around. The shepherd boy laughed loudly at them. He played the same trick on a few more occasions, so the villagers began to doubt his cries.

It so happened that one day, a wolf actually came. The shepherd boy ran towards the village, shouting, "Help! Wolf!"

The villagers thought that the boy was up to his old trick again. "A wolf is attacking my sheep. Please help me," he cried desperately.

But the villagers laughed at him. As the boy kept pleading, the villagers reluctantly went to the spot. But by the time they reached there, they found that the wolf had killed many of the boy's sheep.

86 The Fighting Cocks and the Eagle

Some time ago, two cocks were fighting over a dunghill. Both of them were fighting with all their strength to defeat the other, because the winner would be the ruler of the dunghill. At long last, one cock won as the other one fell after getting wounded severely. The beaten one crept into a hen's house. The winner flew up to a loft and crowed at the top of his voice to announce his success. An eagle was flying by. He darted down on the cock and carried him away. Witnessing the whole thing from the hen's house, the other cock came out and took his position. He announced himself to be the ruler. Pride goes before defeat.

87 The Elephant and the Pack of Jackals

A pack of jackals saw an elephant and wanted to make him their food. One old jackal said, "I know a way by which we can kill him."

The elephant was roaming here and there when he met the old jackal. "Sir, I am a jackal. I have come as the representative of all other animals. We had a meeting and we concluded that we should have a king here. You have all the qualities of a king in you. So please follow me, we'll be grateful if you take the charge."

The elephant was very flattered to hear this. He followed the jackal. The jackal took him to a lake where the elephant slipped and got stuck in thick mud.

"Help me my friend," shouted the elephant helplessly. The jackal smirked viciously and said, "Sir, you trusted someone like me. Now you must pay for it with your life."

The elephant was stuck there and as time passed by, he died. The jackals had a great feast of his flesh.

88 The Quack Frog

Long ago, there was a frog. He remained, most of the time, under the muddy swamp. He had misconceived notions about his abilities to cure everyone. One day, he emerged out of the muddy swamp and claimed to cure all the diseases of the earth. "O friends, do visit me. I have been bestowed with a miraculous power to heal everyone's diseases," he cried at the top of his voice. A fox was passing by. He stopped there and loudly said, "You are a quack doctor. If you are blessed with a miraculous power, why could you not cure your limping or your porous skin? So the self-proclaimed physician, heal yourself first. Man's professions can only be tested in his practice."

89 The Disobedient Son

A merchant had a disobedient, irreligious son. Intending to rouse his interest in religion, his mother sent him to listen to a saint's sermons in the temple; she promised to give him a thousand rupees if he attended the whole session. The greedy son agreed at once. But instead of listening to the saint's teachings, he slept during the entire session.

Next morning, the son came home, took a thousand rupees from his mother and started making plans for moving overseas to trade. His mother pleaded with him not to go, but the man refused to listen to her. He packed his things and left for the voyage. But alas! His ship met with a terrible storm on the way, sinking all passengers on board.

Thus the son paid the price of disobedience.

90 The Fox without a Tail

A fox once survived the attack of hunters, but he lost his tail. Feeling ashamed of his appearance, he decided to do something to save his face. He called a meeting of the foxes and said, "I have had a revelation, my worthy brothers, and I have got rid of my tail by divine instruction. I am leading a happy and easy life now. Our tails are ugly and burdensome. Strange that we do not clip them by our own will. I suggest you follow me and cut down your tails too."

A sly fox stood up, chuckled and said, "Had I lost my tail, I would have found your proposal very convincing. But I still have it, and I see no reason why I or anyone else should cut it. We must avoid suggestions given out of selfishness."

91 The Crow and the Pitcher

It was a hot summer day, and a crow was feeling very thirsty. Looking all around for water, he saw a pitcher, flew up and peeped inside. But the pitcher was empty except for a little water at the very bottom. The crow knew he had to overturn the pitcher or break it, but he did not have the strength to do either. However, he did not lose hope and looked around to find something that could solve the problem. He found a heap of pebbles lying close to the pitcher, and it gave him an idea. The crow carried the pebbles one by one and dropped them into the pitcher. As the pebbles piled up inside, the water level rose and gradually reached the brim. The crow drank to his satisfaction. Necessity is the mother of invention.

92 The Fisherman and the Hunter

A hunter was coming down the mountains loaded with game. Suddenly, he came across a fisherman carrying a bag full of fish. The two met and, in a few minutes' conversation, became friends.

The fisherman longed to eat game, and the hunter expressed his desire to have a dinner of fish. So they happily exchanged their catch. They soon made it a habit of meeting and exchanging their catch every day. One day, while they were eating together, a wise man came up. He noticed the exchange, thought for a while and then said, "My friends, if you keep doing this on a regular basis, soon you will lose the pleasure of sharing. Pleasure is best attained through abstinence."

93 The One-Eyed Doe

A one-eyed doe used to graze near the seaside. She knew she had to be constantly on the alert to save herself from any sudden attacks from hunters. So, she always kept an eye on the surrounding fields presuming that the hunters would come by that route. She never watched the sea, as it didn't occur to her that hunters could approach through the water. One day, some men came rowing by in a boat. Seeing the doe grazing there, they aimed their arrows at her, and in no time she was shot to the ground. The doe, breathing her last, said to herself, "How strange are the ways of destiny! I thought the land was dangerous. But my enemy attacked me from the side I thought was safe."

Danger often comes from the source least suspected.

94 The King Cobra and the Ants

Long ago, a huge king cobra lived in a dense forest. He hunted during the nights and slept during the day. As time passed, he grew so fat that it became difficult for him to squeeze in and out of his hole in the tree. So, he went in search of another tree.

Finally, the cobra selected a very big tree as his new home, but there was a large anthill at the foot of the tree. He slithered up to the anthill angrily, spread his hood and said very rudely to the ants, "I am the king of this forest. I don't want any of you around. I order all of you to find some other place to live. Otherwise, be prepared for your end!"

The ants were so united that they were not scared of the cobra. Instead, thousands of ants marched out of the anthill and soon covered the cobra's entire body with stings and bites! The evil snake went away, crying in pain.

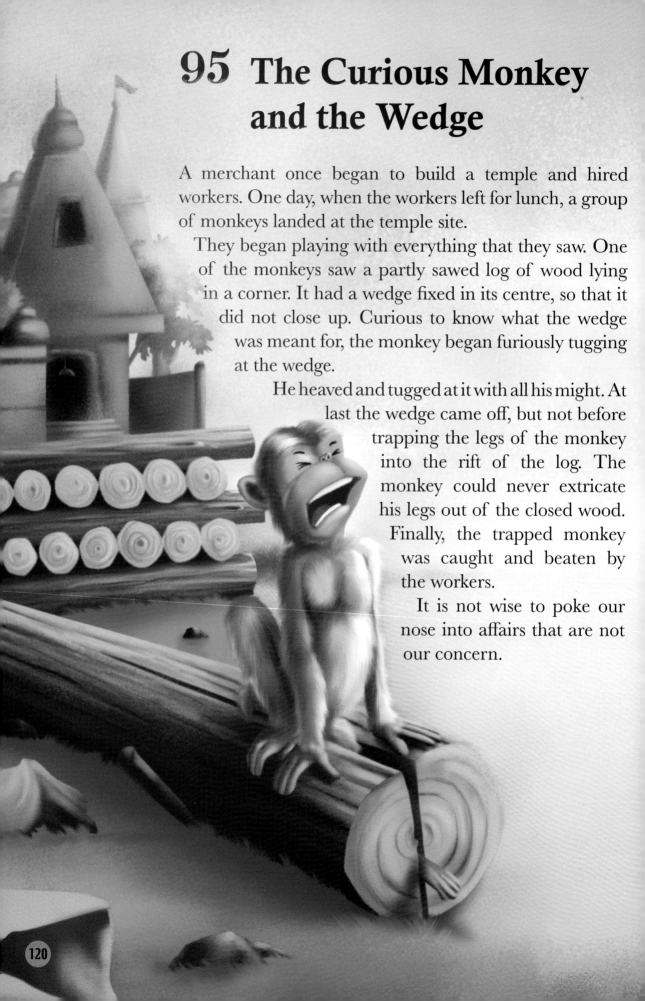

95 The Curious Monkey and the Wedge

A merchant once began to build a temple and hired workers. One day, when the workers left for lunch, a group of monkeys landed at the temple site.

They began playing with everything that they saw. One of the monkeys saw a partly sawed log of wood lying in a corner. It had a wedge fixed in its centre, so that it did not close up. Curious to know what the wedge was meant for, the monkey began furiously tugging at the wedge.

He heaved and tugged at it with all his might. At last the wedge came off, but not before trapping the legs of the monkey into the rift of the log. The monkey could never extricate his legs out of the closed wood. Finally, the trapped monkey was caught and beaten by the workers.

It is not wise to poke our nose into affairs that are not our concern.

96 The Hungry Dogs

There were three dogs who were very close friends. One day, the three dogs were very hungry as they had failed to find any food. Suddenly they saw some bones lying at the bottom of a stream. They tried hard to pick them up, but they were far below their reach. So they decided to drink up all the water of the stream and then get the bones. All three started drinking the water of the stream. After sometime, they felt full and their stomachs were bloated. But still they didn't stop drinking. Their stomachs grew bigger and bigger until they burst open and all the water gushed out. The three dogs now lay dead at the bottom of the stream.

If you attempt the impossible through foolish methods, you are bound to perish.

97 The Dog and the Hare

A dog and a hare happened to be very close friends. The hare was simple in nature while the dog was clever. One day, the dog suddenly caught hold of the hare and bit him hard. The hare was in such pain that he thought he would die. The dog, however, started licking his wound as if he was trying to comfort the hare. The hare was confused at the dog's behaviour and did not know how to respond. He wondered what the dog really wanted. "Tell me first, are you a friend or an enemy? If you are a true friend, why did you bite me so hard? If you are an enemy, then why are you licking my wound? Either kill me or free me so that I can live a life of my own."

A dubious friend is worse than an enemy.

98 The Hen and the Cat

Once upon a time, there was a clever hen. One day, the hen fell ill and was lying in her nest when a cat came to see her. He crept into her nest and said, "My dear friend, how are you? May I help you in any way? I will fetch you whatever you want. Is there anything I can get you right now?"

The hen listened to his over-friendly words and sensed danger.

She said, "Yes, of course. Do me a favour, please. Leave my place. I am sick, and I don't want to run into more trouble by allowing in an unwanted guest."

99 The Monkey and the Crocodile

Once, a monkey and a crocodile were friends. The crocodile's mother, who relished monkey's heart, asked him to get one. The crocodile said to the monkey, "Fruits on the island are ripe. I can take you there." The monkey's mouth watered. He sprang on the crocodile's back and off they went towards the island. Midway, the crocodile revealed, "My mother wants to eat your heart and I am taking you to her." The monkey kept his cool. "Oh, but I left my heart in the tree. You'll have to take me back to get it," said the quick-witted monkey.

The foolish crocodile started back towards the riverbank. No sooner than he reached there, the monkey jumped onto the shore, and capered up the tree to safety.

100 The Ass, the Cock and the Lion

Long ago, an ass and a cock used to live together in a farmyard. One day, a lion was about to pounce on the poor animal when the cock saw what was happening and crowed loudly. The lion took fright at the sudden noise and chose to take to his heels. The ass, noticing the lion running away, was amused. He thought it would fetch him great honour if he chased the king of forest. So he ran after the lion, but suddenly the beast turned and pounced on him. The ass lost his life then and there. Presumption begins in ignorance and ends in ruin.

101 The Beetle Who Challenged the Elephant

One day, a dung beetle spotted some empty liquor bottles on a table. He flew near the bottles, licked the few remaining drops and got drunk. Then, buzzing merrily, he returned to his heap of dung. An elephant passing by, sniffed the dung and feeling disgusted by the foul smell, walked away. The beetle, under the influence of alcohol, imagined that the elephant was frightened of him. He called after the elephant and challenged him to a fight.

"Come on, you big fat fool! Let's fight and see who wins today," he shouted at the elephant. The elephant didn't pay any heed, but the excited beetle continued to jeer at him. Finally, the elephant lost his patience and threw some dung and water on the beetle, killing him instantly. Alcohol gives one false ideas about oneself.

OTHER TITLES
IN THIS SERIES

978-93-81607-39-8

978-93-80069-59-3

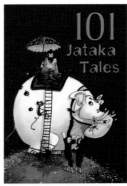

978-93-81607-35-0

978-93-80069-57-9

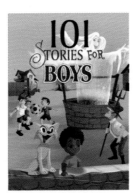

978-93-80070-75-9

978-93-80069-90-6

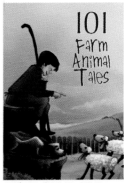

978-93-80069-85-2

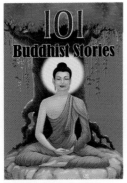

978-93-80069-58-6

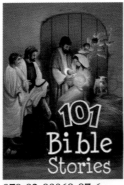

978-93-80069-87-6

978-93-80070-76-6

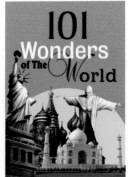

978-93-80070-78-0